HOW TO KEEP
FROM GROWING OLD

GAAR WILLIAMS - BY HIMSELF

HOW TO KEEP FROM GROWING OLD

by

GAAR WILLIAMS

Foreword by
FRANKLIN P. ADAMS

RAND McNALLY & COMPANY

New York   CHICAGO   San Francisco

Designed by Georgette Roux

Dedicated to

L. E. W.

FOREWORD

As a boy in Chicago, who first saw the drawings by John T. McCutcheon in George Ade's *Stories of the Street and of the Town* and his cartoons in the *Chicago Tribune*, I felt later the great debt that so many cartoonists owed to McCutcheon, among them Clare Briggs, H. T. Webster, Jay Darling, and the late — alas! — Gaar Williams. Not that you could get Mr. McCutcheon to say that anybody ever was under his influence. He gave all of these artists no more than their water wings. For before long they cast them aside, and struck out for deep water with sure, bold strokes.

Among the strongest swimmers of his generation — my own midwest generation — was Gaar Williams, a Richmond, Indiana, boy. There were four other Hoosiers equipped with the same sort of picture memory that was Williams' greatest asset. Not counting John T. McCutcheon, there were George Ade of Kentland; Booth Tarkington of Indianapolis; Kin Hubbard, who, though born in Ohio, was so closely identified with Brown County that he was a Hoosier at heart; and James Whitcomb Riley of Greenfield. Each of them drew strongly on the memories of youth and adolescence. And although most of us cannot write or draw, it is a fact that all of us remember the small happenings and the tragedies of our early days much better than what happened last year or even last week. Almost daily it is brought home to me that I cannot remember with whom I had dinner two weeks ago, but I can recall who sat where in each room in Douglas School, Chicago. I know which teacher taught which room, and I can sing all the songs that I heard at the Olympic Theater between 1896 and 1899. So while I marvel at those who can put into words or pictures the memories of youth, I feel that it is not so wonderful an ability as I once thought it.

I was filled with both wonderment and satisfaction, however, when I looked at Gaar Williams' pictures of life in a small town, for in my youth Chicago was a succession of small towns. We hitched on horsecars, cutters, ice wagons. And when I was eight, Mr. Louis Weinberg, the butcher, often let me hold the horse while he delivered the meat orders from his butcher shop — a shop whose floor was covered with sawdust and whose window had a continuous spray of water to keep the vegetables cool.

It is not only that the countless things Gaar Williams recalled from boyhood and young manhood are almost what I recall; he opens up a flood of memories for millions of Americans. It is true that the Williams pictures are as American as Abraham Lincoln, baseball, and Sinclair Lewis.

The picture-makers who have best shown us ourselves — Briggs and Webster and McCutcheon and the Williams of AMONG THE FOLKS IN HISTORY and HOW TO KEEP FROM GROWING OLD — remembered the days of boyhood. But they — and especially Williams — have done their country a great service. They have made a contribution to American history (though it seems to me that Williams would have called that description pretentious). Like other important commenters on their country's history (I except the Gibbonses and the McMasterses and even the Parkmans), the historical part of the cartoonists' work was not consciously done. Perhaps the most conspicuous person to have worked in the unplanned manner of commenting on history was Samuel Pepys, Secretary of the Admiralty. His *Diary* is most valuable for the trivia, the human and universal things —what he had for dinner, the Shakespeare and other plays that he saw and what he thought of them, his marital and extra-marital relations, what he paid for his clothes. These tell more about what life was like in the days of Charles II than do the conscious histories of the time.

Gaar Williams drew in the well-remembered days of the Twenties — the days of the Franklin, the Auburn, the Peerless, the Pierce Arrow, and the Model T Ford. It was the time when touring was an adventure. It was the day of the Blue Book, when road signs were painted on trees, and motorists read, "Follow trolley, bear right at monument on left. 81.4."

It was the day when few of us had radios. In the Smith-Hoover campaign of 1928 I had to go six miles to a friend's house to listen to the candidates, to hear Franklin D. Roosevelt, at the Democratic Convention in New York, speak of Al Smith as "the Happy Warrior." John Held, Jr., at that time my neighbor in Weston, Connecticut, was in the heavy dough drawing the leggy and gartered flapper.

Thousands of us went to Florida. It was in the late Twenties and early Thirties when too many bought lots and lakes in that lovely state, and lost Big Money. Gene Tunney defeated Jack Dempsey twice, and Big Bill Tilden was national lawn tennis champion, and Helen Wills dominated the women. Movies were silent.

Gertrude Ederle came home having swum the English Channel, and was greeted at City Hall in New York by Mayor James J. Walker. Charles Lindbergh, the day my son, now twenty-one, was weaned, made his still celebrated trip to Paris. Edna Ferber's *So Big* and Sinclair Lewis' *Elmer Gantry* were best sellers — books written by a Michigan girl from Kalamazoo, and a Minnesota boy from Sauk Center. I was on the staff of the *New York World*, and wrote a column of devastating satire about the first issue of the *New York Daily News*. The *World* sank in February, 1931, with all on board; the *New York Daily News* has the largest circulation in the United States. Gaar Williams' pictures were syndicated in the *News*.

It was a time when a Mr. Hayward Kendall offered Cornell University a lot of money if it would forswear "its devotion to caste, as in fraternities, to sex, and to the bare knees of the girl students." "But" — and I quote myself of June 28, 1928 — "I read no further, it being like my offering the descendants of King Canute $10,000,000 if they would make the ocean waves rise and fall at their command." It was the brief day of miniature golf, mah jong, Dr. Coué, bathtub gin, the speak-easy, and the hip flask.

And in How to Keep from Growing Old, Williams reflects much of that lush, pre-Hitler, pre-*New Yorker* period. But none of the sinful practices of this era was depicted in the gentle pictures he drew. He was concerned with such signs of modernity as the radio, and the motor car, which he showed in dozens of ways, including cars on the way to Florida through the snow. His attention was focused primarily on human traits and foibles which are as valid today as they were twenty years ago and as they will be twenty years from now.

Old-fashioned — happily — is the idea that it is sort of effeminate for boys to do well at school. Otherwise it is hard to realize that a boy with the uncanny mnemonic ability of Gaar Williams failed three times in Latin, and that he was supposed to be a poor speller. Well, I will give 50 to 1 that his Latin teacher was at fault; and a cartoonist is seldom known as a good speller. The words to his pictures occur in capitals. A lower-case writer who may be an orthographical wizard often has trouble writing ten or twenty words all in capitals. Try it yourself sometime, you spelldown champs!

In spite of the fact that Latin was a weak point in Gaar Williams' schooling, it occurs to me, whose strong point was Latin and whose weak one was history, that the alternate title to both AMONG THE FOLKS IN HISTORY and HOW TO KEEP FROM GROWING OLD might be "Forsitan et haec olim meminisse juvabit," meaning, translated, "What fun it will be sometime to have remembered these things!"

How I wish that he were still doing those pictures!

—FRANKLIN P. ADAMS

HOW TO KEEP
FROM GROWING OLD

CHALLENGE

WHITE WATER

INVITATION

URBAN WOODSMEN

VOICES OF DAWN

ADOLESCENCE

MAN AND MOUSE

À LA MODE

REDUCING

SAMSON II

OPTIMIST

STUNT MAN

CAUTIOUS TUTOR

LIFE OF EASE

BOOBY TRAP

THE MIDNIGHT ALARM

VOLUNTEER

WISHFUL THINKER

CAMERA FAN

LOUD SPEAKER

RETALIATION

REACTION

WELL REMEMBERED

AMBUSH

SHORT CUT

STUMBLING BLOCK

UNSUCCESSFUL EXPERIMENT

UNENDURABLE PROVOCATION

IMPERFECT MEMORY

YOUTH

UNWELCOME VISITOR

STALWART

GAAR
WILLIAMS + DOC. P

NATURALIST

THERE ARE TIMES WHEN WE'RE TEMPTED TO TRY TO THUMB OUR WAY.

- GAAR WILLIAMS -

AMBITION

DEFLATIONIST

FRESH-AIR FIEND

HOME-STATE ROOTER

FORMAL DRESS

MOTHER'S HELPER

UNKNOWN GROUND

HOME-TOWN BOY

TRYING TO READ
YOUR OWN HANDWRITING
IN A SHOPPING CROWD.
— GAAR
WILLIAMS.

THE MADDING CROWD

TRY TO GET THE FAMILY BUS HOME SAFELY IN THE 1 A.M. TRAFFIC.

Reg. U. S. Pat. Off.: Copyright. 1927, by The Chicago Tribune.

NIGHT OUT

PART-TIME HANDYMAN

MYOPIA

CURIOSITY

ROAD HOG

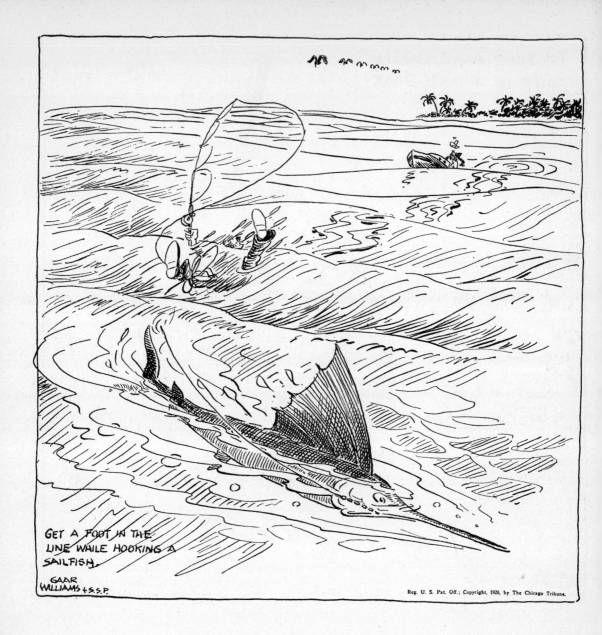

GET A FOOT IN THE
LINE WHILE HOOKING A
SAILFISH.

GAAR
WILLIAMS + S.S.P.

WINTER VACATION

TRY SOME ANNIE OAKLEY
STUFF IN A DUCK BOAT.

SHOW OFF

MINOR IRRITATION

UNACCUSTOMED ENERGY

ACQUISITION

SELF-CONFIDENCE

HELPMEET

UNSEEING EYE

VIRGIN TERRITORY

MORNING CALL

SPRING SONG

BACK TO YOUTH

FREEDOM ROAD

IN THE BALANCE

THE MOTOR BOAT ENTHUSIAST LETS HIS ACTIVITIES LAP OVER INTO THE DUCK SEASON.

Reg. U. S. Pat. Off.; Copyright, 1931, by The Chicago Tribune.

OUT OF BOUNDS

INVENTOR

JANUARY CLEARANCE

BRIEF INTERLUDE

POLAR BEAR

SUPERSTITION

RESIGNATION

LAST STRAW

ORIENTAL INFLUENCE

PUBLIC BEACH

PENDULUM OF HISTORY

AMATEUR TALENT

MAMA'S DARLING

EXCURSION

DETERMINATION

PROUD POSSESSOR

PIONEERS

CONQUEROR

BUTTERFINGERS

PERSEVERANCE